FOSSIL FUEL FRENZY!

BY
ROBIN TWIDDY

POLLUTED PLANET

BookLife
PUBLISHING

©2019
BookLife Publishing
King's Lynn
Norfolk, PE30 4LS

All rights reserved.
Printed in Malaysia.

A catalogue record for this book is available from the British Library.

ISBN: 978-1-78637-525-4

Written by:
Robin Twiddy

Edited by:
Kirsty Holmes

Designed by:
Drue Rinfoul

PHOTO CREDITS

CONTENTS

Words that look like this are explained in the glossary on page 31.

WELCOME STUDENTS

The Year: 3025

Location: The space station Atrahasis orbiting
New Earth – formerly known as Mars

Population: 753

Onboard the space station, in its cutting-edge classroom, a new generation of human children are beginning their most important lesson.

Pronunciation guide: Atrahasis = ah-trah-**hah**-sis

Welcome, students. You will be the first generation to set foot on New Earth, now that the **terraforming** process is finally complete. The future of humanity rests on your shoulders.

Before you can make a home on New Earth, you must learn about the fate of Earth One: the **consequences** of the greed of the human race, and the ultimate destruction of the planet. It is said that those who do not remember the past are doomed to repeat it. We cannot afford to repeat this mistake!

Earth One

This course will teach you about fossil fuels: what they are, how they were formed, how they changed human society and, most of all, how a lack of understanding early brought about the **extinction** of the human race.

LESSON 1:
FOSSIL FUELS 101

The first lesson begins with the basics. What are fossil fuels? Where do they come from? And why were they so important?

It took millions of years for fossil fuels to form deep under the surface of Earth One. Fossil fuels can take the form of coal, crude and heavy oil, and natural gas.

COAL

Formed from giant plants that existed before the dinosaurs, these plants piled up when they died and eventually were **compacted** under soil and dirt. Pressure and heat changed the layers of plants into coal over millions of years.

CRUDE AND HEAVY OIL

Oil was formed from the remains of small animals and plants that fell to the bottom of the ocean and were covered by sediment and trapped. Like coal, it was slowly changed over millions of years.

NATURAL GAS

Natural gas was formed in the same way as oil, with the exception that different temperatures, levels of pressure and type of **biomass** resulted in the production of gas instead of oil.

The energy within those plants and animals became trapped. People discovered that burning these fossil fuels would release this trapped energy.

Coal was burned to provide heat, and for **smelting**, as far back as the **Bronze Age**. During the Industrial Revolution (between 1760 and 1820), steam-powered machines changed the way things were made. This is when the use of coal and oil increased, and began to change the world.

Everyone loved coal — but little did they know of the horror hidden in that soot and smoke!

Lots of new technologies were developed at this time. Coal was used to power steam engines in steam trains, steam boats and steam-powered factories. This made coal very valuable.

Around the same time, the first electric power station was built. Soon, electric lines would be running to every home in every town and it would become normal to have electrical power.

The invention of the **internal combustion engine** made oil even more valuable than coal. Oil could be **refined** into petrol that powered the internal combustion engine. By the late **20th century**, most homes had a car powered by petrol or diesel – both were made with crude oil. Altogether, the Industrial Revolution had made people's lives easier and more comfortable.

LESSON 3:
BIG BUSINESS

Oil became big business. But soon, people began to realise that it was a non-renewable resource; once the oil was gone, it would take hundreds of millions of years for supplies to begin to **replenish**.

Oil Derrick

Although lots of money was put into drilling for oil and transporting it, accidents were still quite common. Between 1967 and 2010 there were over 13 major oil spills. When an oil spill gets into an **ecosystem**, it clings to everything. It can be absorbed by plants and soil, making entire areas unsuitable for life.

Some companies illegally dumped dangerous oil by-products straight into the environment to save money.

FIGHTING FOR FUEL

It seemed that fossil fuels had changed the world for the better, but when people realised that they wouldn't last forever, the trouble began. Wars broke out over the remaining oil supplies. Lots of lives were lost.

Rather than investing in renewable energy sources, some nations tried to take control of territories with oil reserves. These wars resulted in more oil than ever being used to transport troops, **manufacture** weapons, and as fuel for tanks and planes.

LESSON 4:
THE HIDDEN COST

People didn't realise at first, but burning fossil fuels released carbon dioxide (CO_2) into the atmosphere. By 2018, burning fossil fuels had produced around 21.3 billion tonnes of CO_2 per year. Before the Industrial Revolution, only small amounts of fossil fuel were burned. The Earth could cope with this. Parts of the Earth, such as the oceans and forests, absorb CO_2 as part of the natural balance. These are known as carbon sinks.

The atmosphere of a planet balances the **radiation** coming into the planet and leaving it. Earth had an atmosphere that **regulated** the temperature. New Earth's atmosphere has just been completed and is currently perfectly balanced.

New Earth

So, you may ask, how did this atmosphere work? Gases in the atmosphere, known as greenhouse gases, stopped too much heat from leaving the planet. These gases were:

WATER VAPOUR

CARBON DIOXIDE

METHANE

When energy from the Sun entered Earth's atmosphere, the greenhouse gases would trap some of that energy, and this would help keep the planet at a temperature that was **habitable** for humans and other life. Until the Industrial Revolution, the amounts of these gases in the atmosphere had stayed stable for a long time.

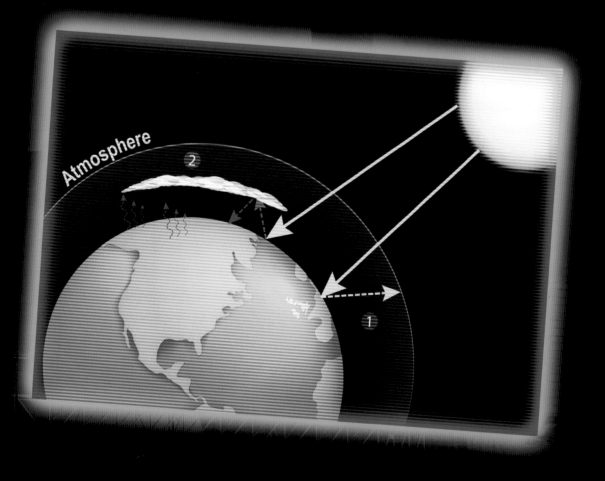

The people of Earth One were burning fossil fuels for everything: for electricity, to fuel cars, lorries, planes and ships, and even manufacturing plastic. All of this added more and more CO_2 to the atmosphere.

In 2018, 99% of plastics were made from fossil fuels.

At first, people did not understand that this would affect the climate of the planet. But it soon became clear that this was a real problem. By the early 2000s it was clear that the climate was changing, but still people did not change their ways.

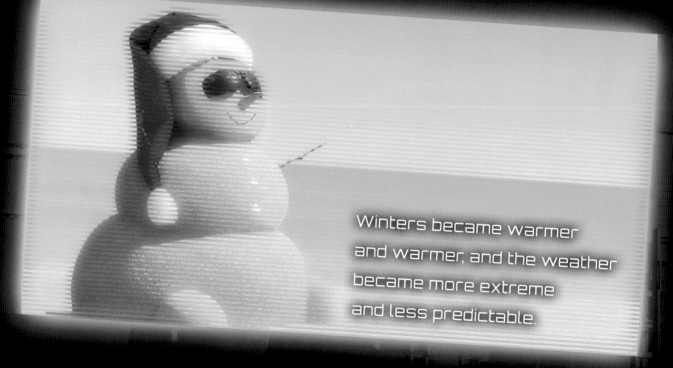

Winters became warmer and warmer, and the weather became more extreme and less predictable.

THE OTHER COSTS

Aside from the effects of CO_2 on the climate, burning fossil fuels polluted the air directly. Burning fossil fuels released sulphur dioxide (SO_2), nitrogen oxides (NOx) and particulate matter (soot) into the air.

This air pollution led to an increase in diseases such as asthma, lung cancer, leukaemia, and pneumonia. By the mid-21st century, people needed air purifiers in their homes and respirators when in cities. The air around cities filled with smog, the likes of which had not been seen since the famous London 'pea-soup' smog of 1952.

LESSON 5:
TOO HOT TO HANDLE

During the late 21st century, the amount of CO_2 in the atmosphere led to an extreme rise in temperature. This led to the melting of the polar ice caps and resulted in flooding and, at times, **megatsunamis** caused by giant ice sheets falling into the ocean.

To avoid the flooding coastlines, people moved farther inland. This meant that inland areas became overcrowded. These areas were not big enough to handle so many people. There was not enough food or power for all the coastal **refugees** when they arrived.

By 2105, the overall temperature of Earth One had risen so much that the **Equator** had become uninhabitable. The heat meant that 50% of crops failed, leaving many starving. The temperature alone made it impossible for any type of life to survive. First, the animals began to migrate towards the poles where the planet was a little cooler; then the people followed.

At this point things were looking very bleak for humanity. The air was thick with smog and toxins, the seas had risen to swallow whole cities and temperatures had risen so much that most other areas were uninhabitable. Something had to be done!

- The red area shows areas that are so hot that a human being would be cooked alive.

- The green arrows show the migrating people forced from their homes by the heat.

LESSON 6:
TOO LITTLE, TOO LATE

Before things became too bad, people had tried to make a difference. Alternatives to fossil fuels (including solar, wind and water power) were used. These clean, renewable energy sources were much better for the environment, and wouldn't ever run out.

But it was too late. The damage had already been done! And not everybody was on-board with these alternatives. Some people still did not believe in man-made climate change and others were just greedy. They had lots of money invested in coal and oil and did not care about what happened to the environment.

Solar power converts energy from the Sun into electricity. More energy reached Earth One from the Sun in an hour than was ever used in any single year. If only more people had started using this before destroying the planet with fossil fuels.

Renewable energy slowed the destruction of Earth One but could not stop it. People became aware of the problems and protested against the use of oil and coal. They became less wasteful and tried not to use electricity unnecessarily. People walked instead of driving short distances.

The most important thing about clean, renewable energy sources is that they can power all the things that fossils fuels can but without destroying the environment. And they will not run out. But it was hard to change people's attitudes because it meant changing how they lived their lives.

Familiarise yourselves with these **blueprints** for wind turbines. These are the same ones that you will be using on New Earth.

Wind turbines are an excellent alternative for generating electricity. They do not produce any greenhouse gases, they take up very little room and do not use up any water. Unfortunately, lots of people thought that they were ugly and ruined the landscape. If only those people had lived to see the landscape now!

Hydroelectricity is another alternative means of generating electricity, using the movement of water to turn a turbine and power the generator.

These can be made using dams that redirect water over the turbine blades, or by using the natural movement of water in coastal areas.

You will need to understand hydro and tidal power plants. You will be using these on New Earth.

It is these renewable energy sources that you will use on New Earth: a combination of solar power, wind power and hydro power. These will provide everything that you need. All the transport on New Earth uses clean electricity.

These are some of the energy sources on New Earth.

LESSON 7:
THE SOVEREIGN NATION OF THE SOUTH POLE

By 2195, the global temperature had risen to such an extreme level that a mass migration to Antarctica began. All the other continents were now too hot for any living things, and the world was like a giant dustbowl. Refugees from all the nations travelled across the desert that was once Argentina, and then by boat to the last resort: Antarctica.

Many people did not make it.

War, famine, pollution and the heat had reduced the world's population from 7.6 billion in 2018 to 5.8 million in 2197. The remaining people formed a new nation: the Sovereign Nation of the South Pole or SNSP for short.

They knew that it was only a matter of time before even this last refuge could no longer support them. They began working on a plan to escape the world they had failed. Even though the temperature had risen and Antarctica was now warmer than ever before, there were still big problems. During the winter there were only three hours of sunlight a day! This made growing crops difficult.

The leaders gathered together the greatest minds of the SNSP and began to plan a new society. Because hot air rises and cool air sinks, the difference between the temperature of the land and the sea in 2197 caused the Antarctic wind to be extremely strong and constant. Although this made living there difficult, it was perfect for generating electricity with wind turbines.

LESSON 8:
THE GREAT EXODUS

Using technology from old research stations, the Sovereign Nation of the South Pole built and launched this space station, the Atrahasis, to house the last of mankind until we could make a new planet habitable.

This is the Atrahasis orbiting Mars before it was terraformed.

All of the remaining animals of Earth One were also brought into space. These animals have now been sent to New Earth, where they have settled into the new climate. New Earth is a pollution-free world. The fields, oceans, mountains and forests have been filled with life.

Live Feed from New Earth

LIVING ON A SPACE STATION

For the last 105 years, humanity has been living on this: the space station Atrahasis. The station runs entirely on solar power. We have banned all plastic products as they require oil to make and are also a danger to the environment.

Finally, we have a generation of children who have not picked up bad Earth One habits from their parents. While living on this space station, you have had to recycle everything you use. We believe you are ready.

LESSON 9:
A NEW HOPE
– NEW EARTH

That brings us to New Earth. You are humanity's last hope; there will not be another Earth after this one. You must use all of the knowledge you have gained about Earth One and its past in these lessons to make sure that it never happens again.

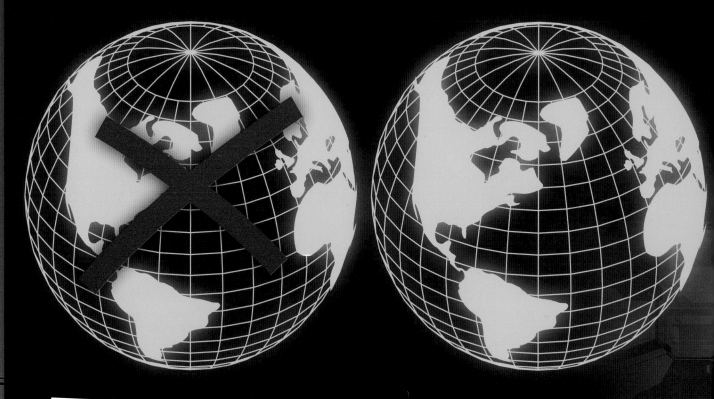

Humans are incredibly inventive and can do some amazing things, but we cannot always see past our own cleverness. It is very important that you learn to live in harmony with nature and do not take it for granted.

When you land on New Earth you will not be alone. There will be other children, but no adults; the adults cannot be trusted to get this right. You will also find that there are lots of familiar animals and plants from Earth One. You will be responsible for all of them, and each other.

Now all you must do is complete the end of term exam. If you pass, you will be issued with your ration packs and space suit, then loaded onto the space shuttle 'A New Start' for transport to New Earth. If you fail, I am afraid you will have to stay here on the space station Atrahasis with all the adults.

SCANNING

SEARCH

COMPLETE

ANALYSIS

FINAL EXAM

Welcome students. This is your final exam. Please be seated and p
your question tablet. Answers can be found on page 32.

Question 1: What are the three types of fossil fuels?

A: Coal

B: Slate

C: Rude Oil

D: Natural Gas

E: Crude Oil

Question 2: List three renewable sources of energy.

Question 3: What are the three greenhouse gases?

Question 4: What greenhouse gas is released when fossil fuels are burned?

Question 5: When was London covered in 'pea soup' smog?

Question 6: Which renewable energy source became more effective in SNSP in 2197?

Question 7: In 2018, what percentage of plastic was made from fossil fuels?

GRADUATION DAY

Congratulations! You have successfully completed your course on humanity's mistakes that led to the end of life on Earth One. You have demonstrated an excellent understanding of the dangers of using fossil fuels and exhausting the natural resources of a planet. You are ready to begin a new life on New Earth, and use what you have learned to make sure New Humanity doesn't repeat the same mistakes. Take care of your new home, recruits.

Prepare for take-off; you leave for New Earth immediately. You and your fellow graduates are making history today. The fate of humanity rests on your shoulders and on the knowledge you have learnt here. The world is in your hands.

WHAT THEY SHOULD HAVE DONE!

Although New Earth is going to make a fine home, things would have been better and billions of lives would have been saved if humanity had done things differently in the beginning.

From 2018 onwards, the pollut from fossil fuels and the effec of global warming could have b slowed or stopped if people ha started making changes – bot and small – to the way they li

Here is a list of things that people could have done:

- Making sure that you walk or ride your bicycle instead of driving or taking the bus.

- Don't waste electricity. Turn off lights and switch things off at the wall when you are not using them.

- Choose companies that use renewable energy.

- Support electric transport.

- Monitor your carbon footprint.

- Use energy-saving light bulbs.

- Repair and reuse. This will save on manufacturing costs.

- Buy locally. This will save on fuel used for transport.

If only people had begun making these small changes in the early 21st century, we would never have had to leave Earth One in the first place.

GLOSSARY

20TH CENTURY	the period of time beginning on the 1st of January 1901 and ending on the 31st of December 2000
BIOMASS	organic material which has stored sunlight as chemical energy
BLUEPRINTS	plans or technical drawings intended to instruct how to build or make a thing
BRONZE AGE	a period of time in early human history when people started using bronze tools, starting around 5,000 years ago
BY-PRODUCTS	the secondary and often unintentional result of production
COMPACTED	the process by which pressure put on sediment causes it to stick together and form rock
CONSEQUENCES	the results or effects of an action
DERRICK	a lifting device, often used when drilling for oil
ECOSYSTEM	a community of living things and the environment they live in
EQUATOR	the imaginary line around the Earth that is an equal distance from the North and South Poles
EXTINCTION	when a whole species of animal or plant dies out
GRADUATES	people who have completed a course of education and received a qualification
HABITABLE	when something is safe to live in
INTERNAL COMBUSTION ENGINE	an engine in which fuel is burned to release energy
MANUFACTURE	to make large quantities of something
MEGATSUNAMIS	giant destructive waves caused by the displacement of a large piece of land into the ocean
RADIATION	the release of energy as waves or particles
REFINED	something that has been made purer by removing materials or substances from it
REFUGEES	people who have been forced to leave their homes in order to escape danger
REGULATED	controlled and maintained
REPLENISH	fill something up again
SMELTING	melting ore to extract the metal
TERRAFORMING	changing a planet to make it habitable

INDEX